For Oscar and Isla
Love from Sam Williams xx

First published in Great Britain in 2018
by Boxer Books Limited.
www.boxerbooks.com

A catalogue record for this book is available from the British Library.
The illustrations were prepared using charcoal and digital colour.
The text is set in Avenir.

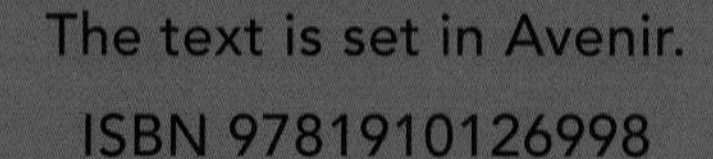

ISBN 9781910126998
1 3 5 7 9 10 8 6 4 2
Printed in China
All of our papers are sourced from managed forests and renewable resources.

10 Blue Butterflies

Sam Williams

Find one red ladybird.

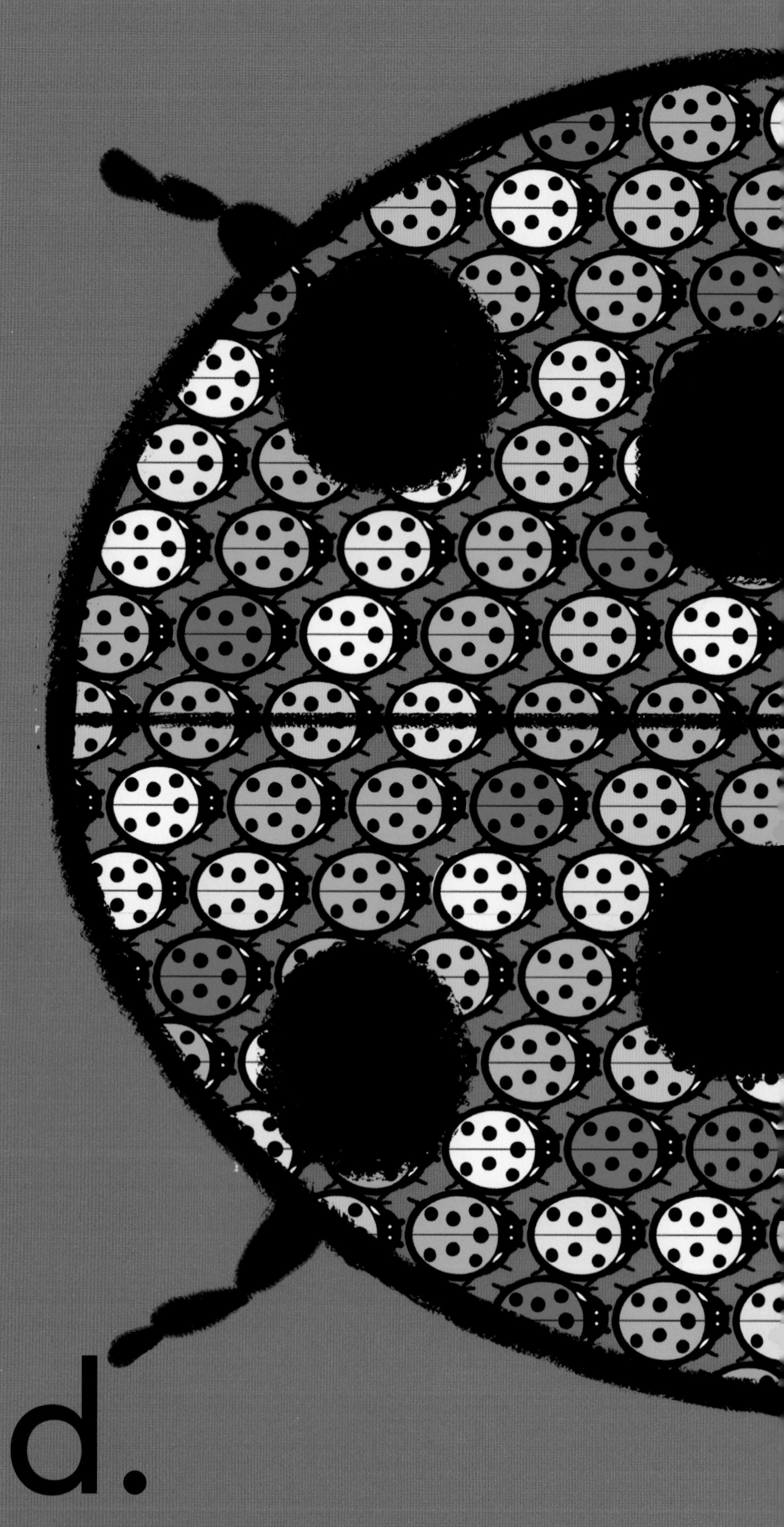

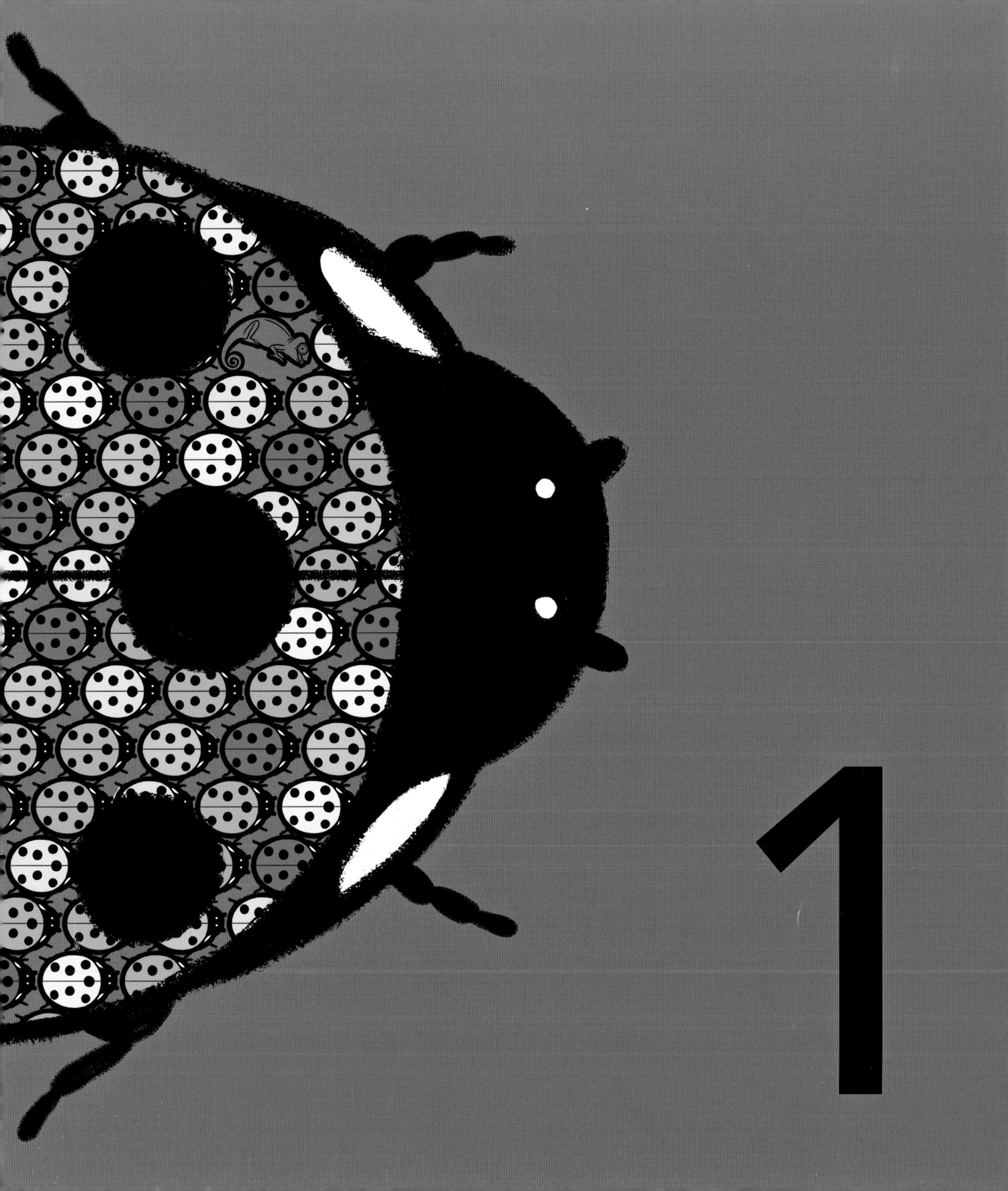
1

Find two orange fish.

2

Find three yellow canaries.

3

Find four green frogs.

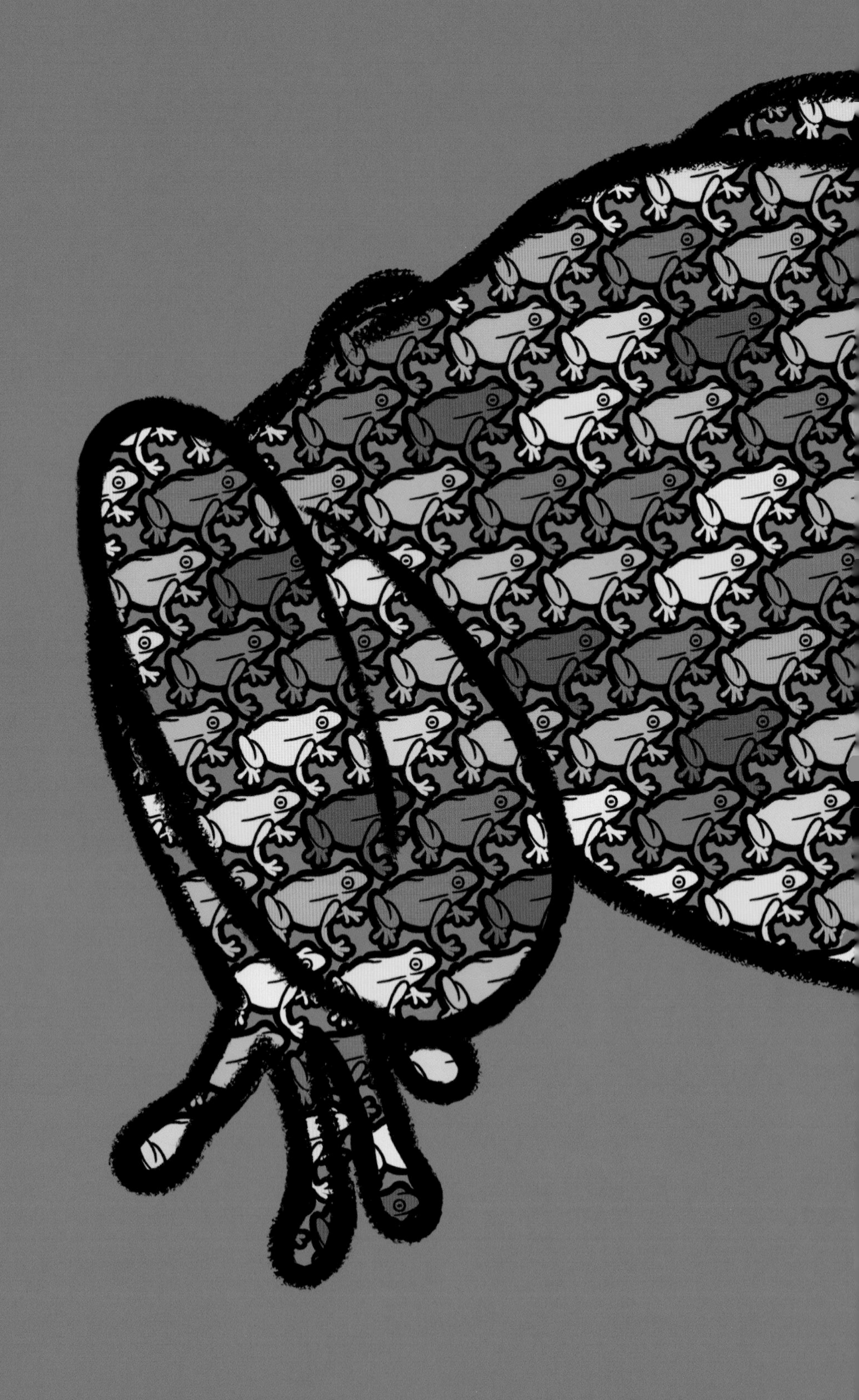

4

Find five white doves.

5

Find six brown bears.

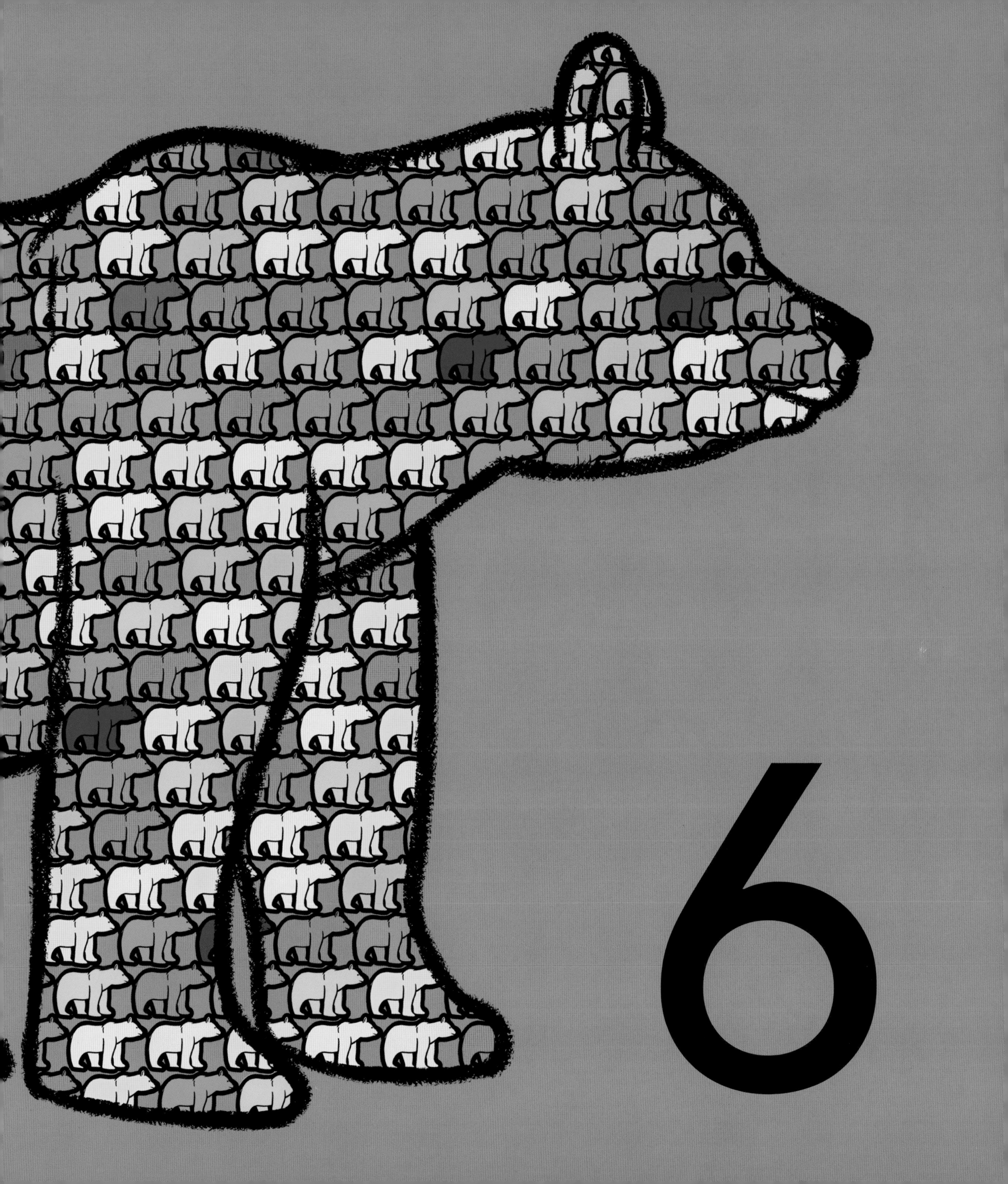
6

Find
seven
grey
seals.

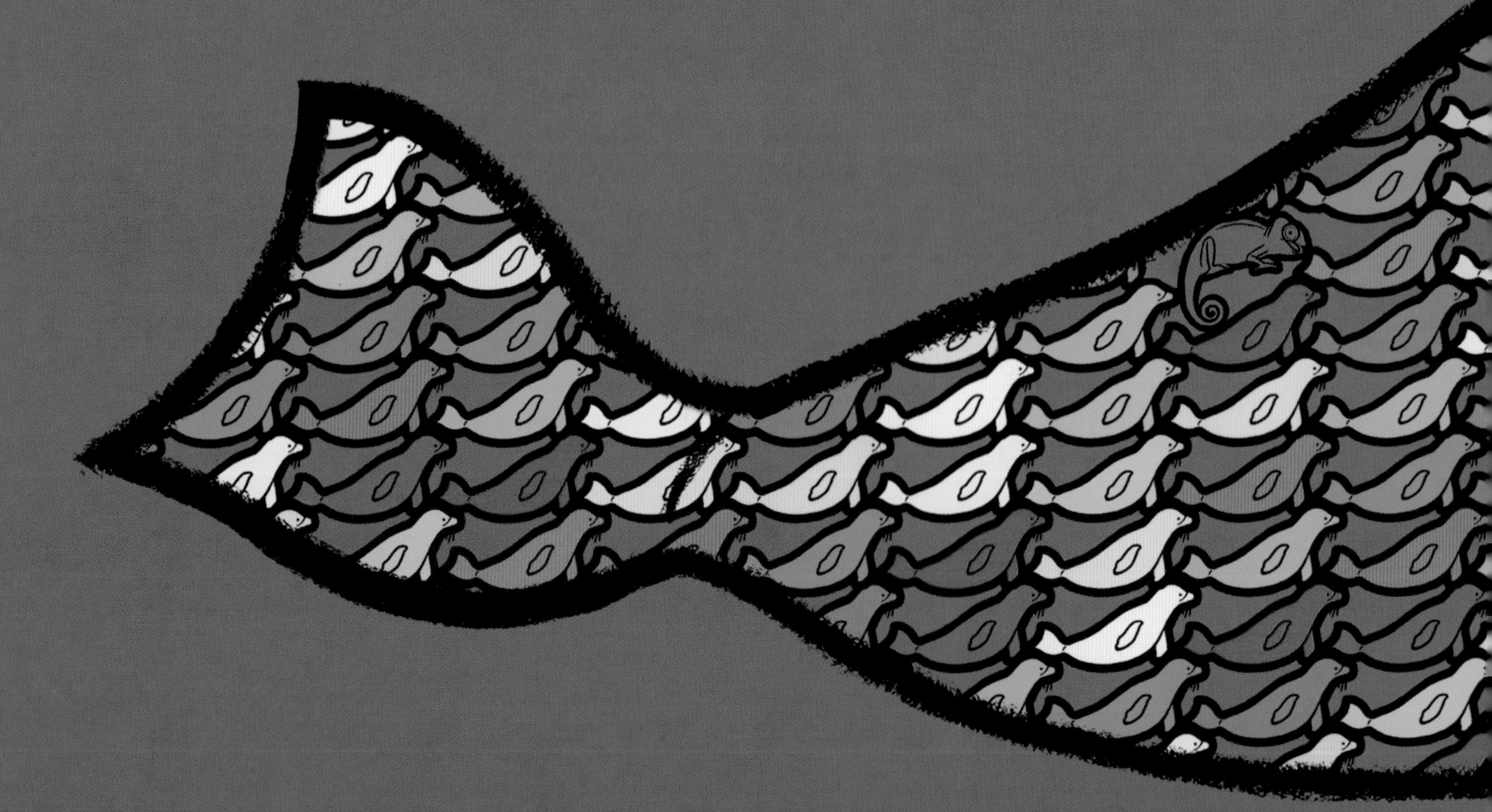

7

Find
eight
black
ponies.

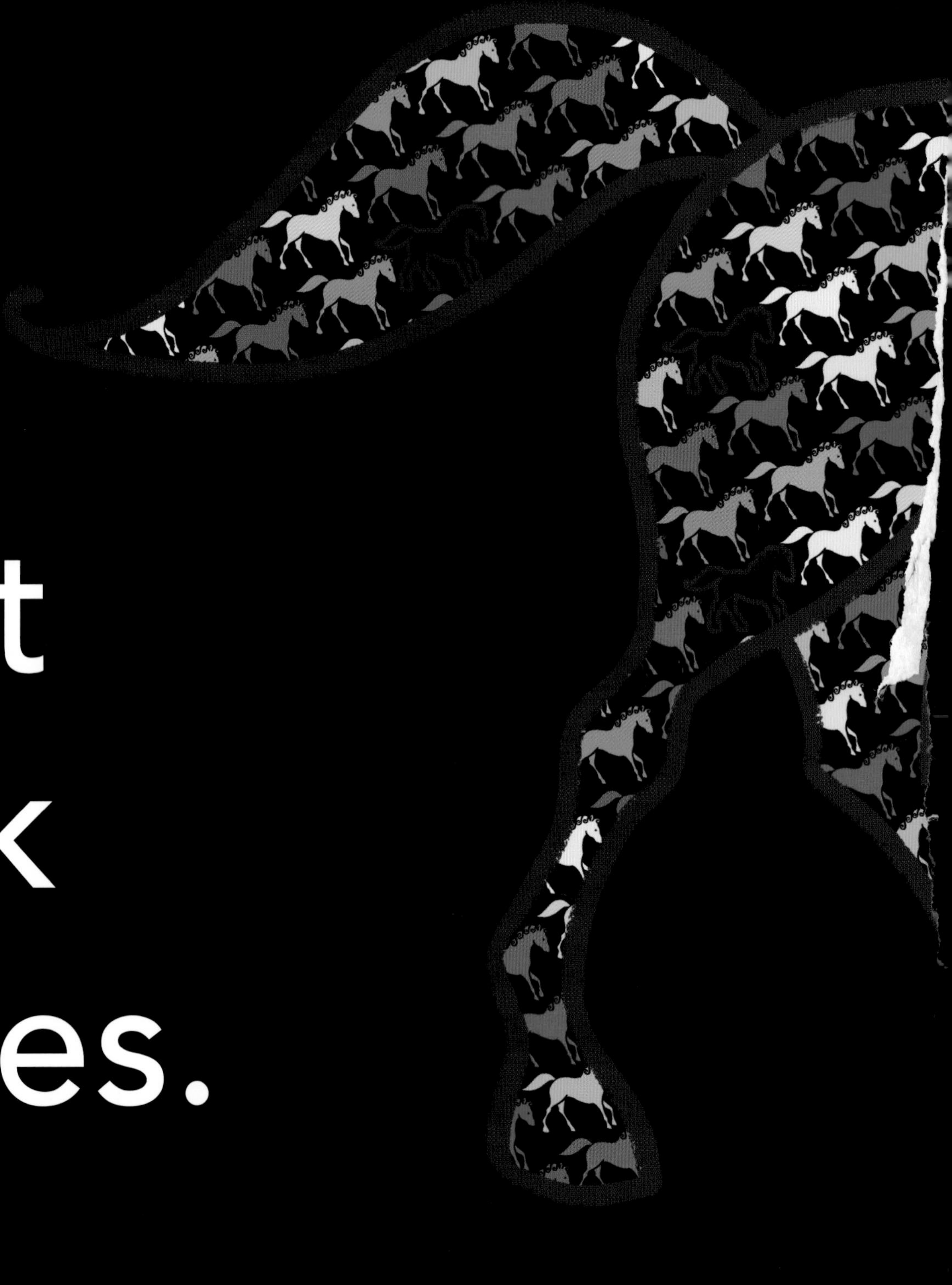

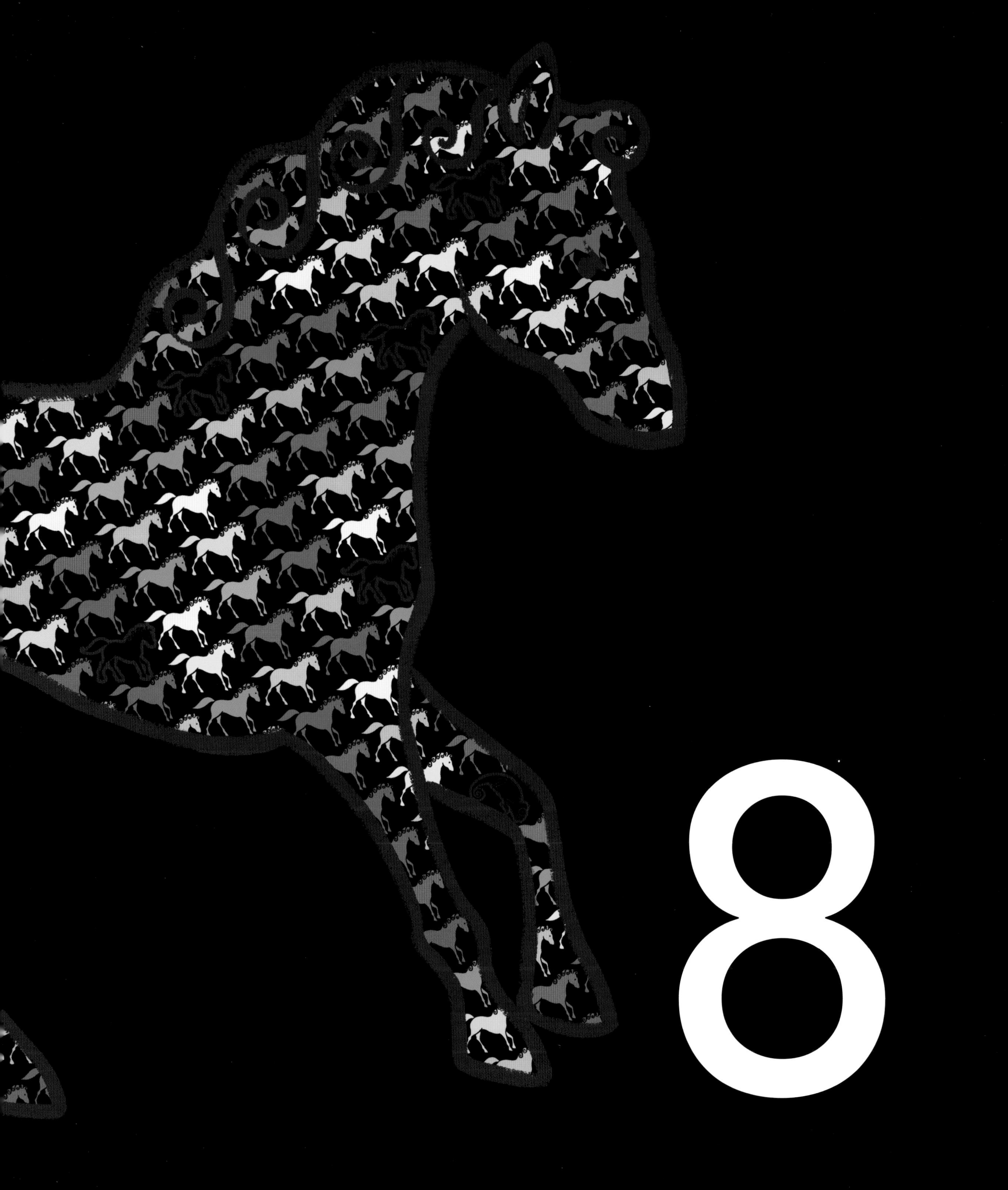
8

Find nine pink flamingos.

Find
ten
blue
butterflies.

10

How many colourful chameleons did you find in this book?

1 red ladybird

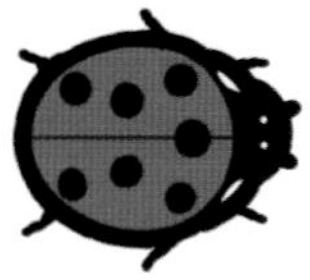

2 orange fish

3 yellow canaries

4 green frogs

5 white doves

6 brown bears

7 grey seals

8 black ponies

9 pink flamingos

10 blue butterflies

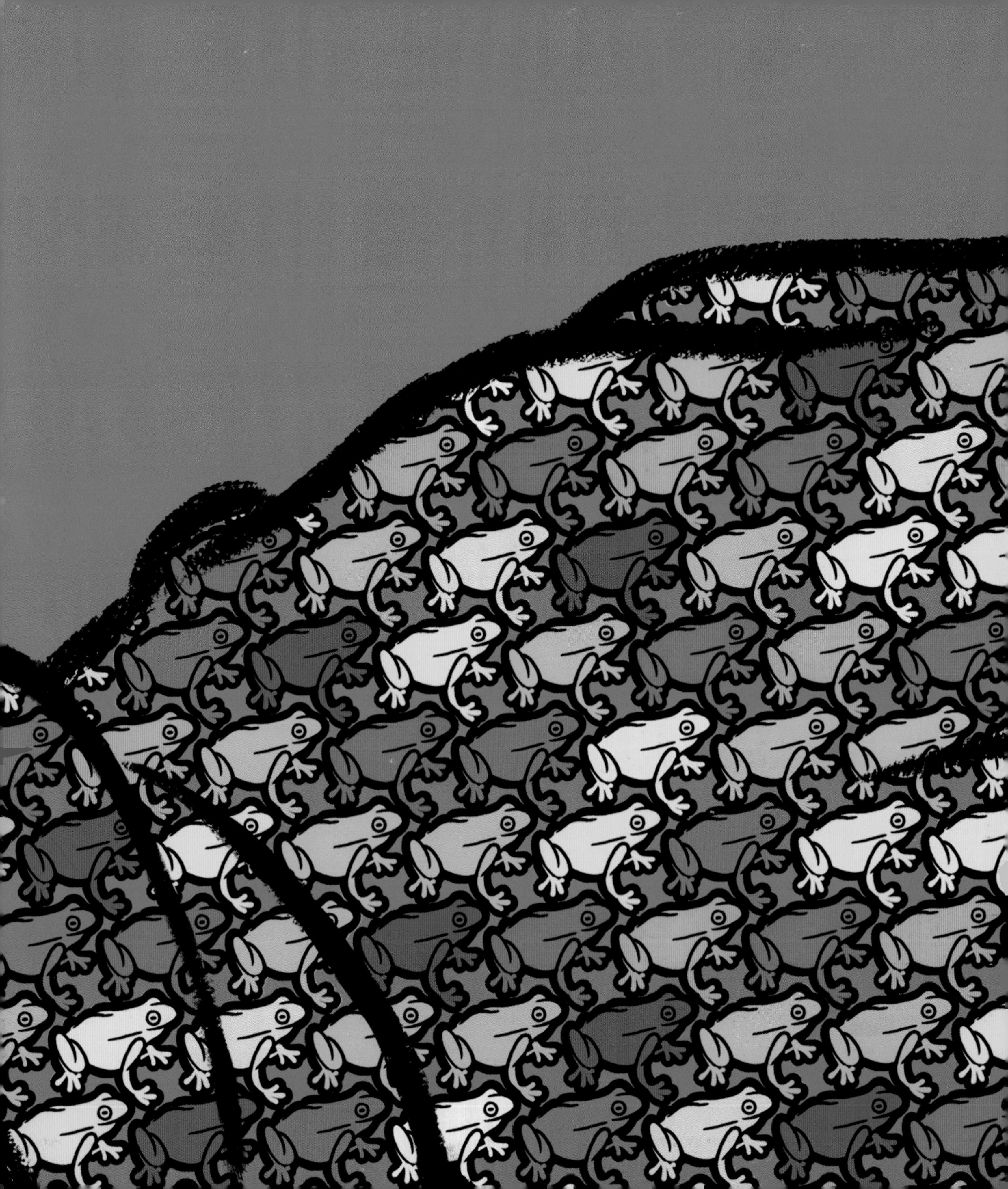